AN UNOFFICIAL GRAPHIC NOVEL FOR MINECRAFTERS

The BATTLE for the DRAGON'S TEMPLE

CARA J. STEVENS
ART BY DAVID NORGREN

SCHOLASTIC INC.

To Mom and Dad,
for giving me roots and wings

No part of this publication may be reproduced, stored in a retrieval system, or transmitted in any form or by any means, electronic, mechanical, photocopying, recording, or otherwise, without written permission of the publisher. For information regarding permission, write to Sky Pony Press, an imprint of Skyhorse Publishing, Inc., 307 West 36th Street, 11th Floor, New York, NY 10018.

ISBN 978-1-338-32804-2

12 11 10 9 8 7 6 5 4 3 2 1   18 19 20 21 22 23

Printed in the U.S.A.   40

First Scholastic printing, September 2018

Special thanks to Cara J. Stevens, David Norgren, and Elias Norgren

Cover design by Brian Peterson
Cover illustrations credit David Norgren
Designer: Joshua Barnaby

INTRODUCTION

If you have played Minecraft, then you know all about Minecraft worlds. They're made of blocks you can mine: coal, dirt, and sand. In the game, you'll find many different creatures, lands, and villages inhabited by strange villagers with bald heads. The villagers who live there have their own special, magical worlds that are protected by a string of border worlds to stop outsiders from finding them.

When we last left off on the small border world of Xenos, Phoenix had just discovered her true parents were dragon slayers who died in their quest to kill the Ender Dragon.

Our story resumes as Phoenix enjoys quiet time back at home. But her stay is far from peaceful. The elders are not happy about Phoenix's presence in the village, and, unable to stop thinking about her parents' failed quest to kill the dragon, Phoenix wonders whether she should remain at home or set out to finish the deed her parents began long ago.

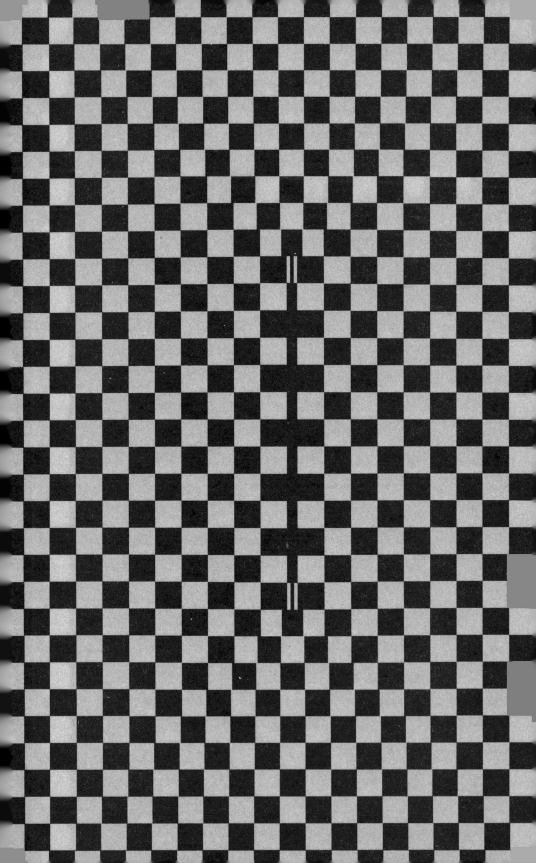

CHAPTER 1

HOME SWEET HOME

...and suddenly, I was surrounded by zombies!

GROOAAAANNN!

Aaaahhhhhh!

Phoenix healed me with a potion and an enchanted golden apple.

Ohhhhhh!

That's not so cool.

But that was just the beginning.

Phoenix and I have been all over the world and conquered more enemies than you've ever heard of.

We will now discuss the matter until we come to a decision. You are free to go.

I think that went well.

I thought they'd agree just to get you to stop talking!

They didn't seem happy when we left.

That's because they'll be stuck in there until all agree.

Do you think we will ever see the village gates open?

I think it was hard enough for them to let Phoenix back in. They're not going to agree to trading with strangers.

We've done all we can for now. I'm going to tell the children. You two rest.

Don't worry, Ole Baba. I'll watch out for Xander.

And he will watch out for you.

And I will watch out for both of them.

Thank you, Moosha.

Ole Baba? Can I ask you a question?

You just did. Do you want to ask another one?

Take that! Oops!

You've been so helpful to us, even though all I do is put everyone in danger.

That's not a question, Phoenix.

I guess I just want to know why.

⹂Grunt⹂

Leila, where are you?

Where did that girl disappear to now?

One day, my parents discovered she had left, so they went after her. There was a terrible lightning storm. My parents never returned. And neither has Leila.

Like Leila, Phoenix, you were born to explore. If the gates were open, it would be safer for explorers like you to see the world.

And if the gates are open, maybe my sister will return.

CHAPTER 2

SECRETS

Slaying the dragon is my quest. Maybe I should go alone.

You don't need to go alone. It's dangerous...

...and we don't want to miss all the fun!

Now that I have been outside the walls, I want to see more!

You can't leave me behind, Phoenix! I promise I'll be helpful.

I'm so happy you want to co with me.

I want to finish what my parents started. And I want to know what's so important about killing the dragon that they gave their lives trying.

We are villagers on a mission to battle the Dragon. If you are reading this, we have failed. Please find our daughter, Violet. You will know her by an enchanted Ender eye necklace, hair the color of apples, and a tiny nose. She is in Elysia with friends. Please take care of our precious girl, and love her as we do, she will protect you and bring peace.

— Flora and D

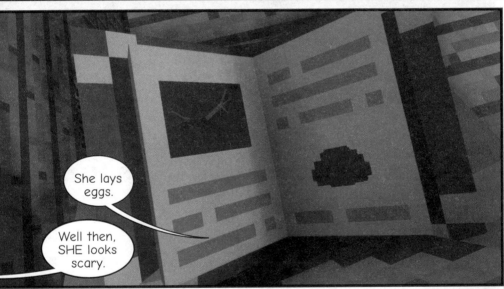

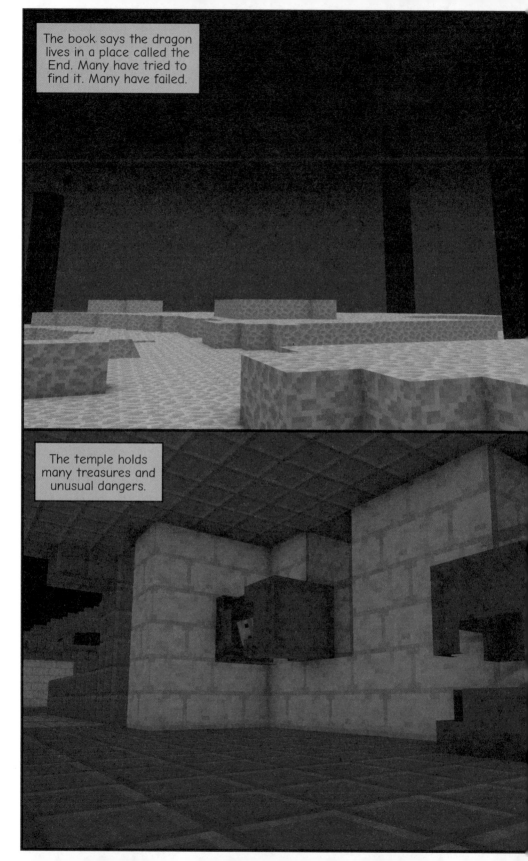

The book says the dragon lives in a place called the End. Many have tried to find it. Many have failed.

The temple holds many treasures and unusual dangers.

Follow me.

BUMP

CLICK!

Maybe it just fell out. I'll check down here...

≶Ouch!≶ Hey, that's the Galactic Alphabet!

Each rune stands for a letter.

Am I crazy, or does that say "PHOENIX"?

It appears to be calling to you.

DEFEAT DRAGON FIND DEMON SCROLLS...What do you think that means?

Come, children. We should let your parents know you're leaving again.

I'm excited for another adventure, but I wish you could guarantee there won't be any more spiders.

Really, Xander? You've fought zombies and skeletons and rescued me from pirates, but you're afraid of spiders?

SPLAT!

⸗Shudder⸗ What can I say? They give me the heebie-jeebies!

were wondering where ou went off to. What ere you doing in the basement?

Please don't be angry.

You're going away again, aren't you?

Oh, just getting some last-minute supplies.

We're not angry, but we do worry about you two.

Come, eat something before you go.

It's best if we don't tell you where they are going so that when the elders ask, you can honestly say you don't know.

Will they be safe?

Out of anyone I've ever met, these kids are the best suited for the job they're about to do.

That doesn't answer my question, Ole Baba.

It's okay, Mom. My amulet has been glowing, so I know I'm doing the right thing.

I just hope the elders don't catch you leaving, or we'll never convince them to open the village gates.

Hey, are you guys ready?

You're going with T.H.? I'm glad. He's a good help.

Keep each other safe.

Coming T.H.!

CHAPTER 3

MOBS AND
ENCHANTMENTS

But the best was desert worl. We should totally go there someday and live off the lan like cowboys--and cowgirls.

We won't be able to do that if they close the gates forever. We won't even be able to see you!

Can we go to one of these worlds soon, while we still can?

Is now soon enough for you?

Yes!

Yes!

POP

Hello Tom! Hello Tom's friends! I've been expecting you.

What is this place?

This is a library seed world. Meet my friend, Merlin.

You have excellent taste in books, young sir.

Hah! He never goes anywhere without it!

I'll have you know it's very useful. It helped me rescue you when you were captured by zombie pigman pirates in the Nether.

I have nothing against your book, Xander. It's just part of you. Like my necklace.

Demon scrolls, you say? I think I read somewhere about...

Ah yes. Here it is. You will find these demon scrolls--or elder scrolls--at the bottom of the sea.

riously? The •ttom of the sea?

Yes. But it's worth it. You can't get to the Ender Dragon without the scrolls.

That solves that mystery.

We have to find the scrolls to get to the dragon.

How did you know we are going to fight the...

But it won't be easy going. You'll have to get past the keeper: the elder guardian.

t me get you some supplies...Frost Walker hantment, Aqua Affinity with respiration... Oh, enchanting is such fun!

You want me to enchant that book for you?

I'm good. Thanks, anyway.

All set. There you go.

Thanks for enchanting our stuff!

So, Merlin, where can we find these undersea scrolls?

The ocean monument just past the Swamp of Abandonment.

That's near the witch's house!

Thank you for your help, Merlin!

Glad I could be of service to you. Say hi to your mom and dad for me.

Ready guys?

POP!

SSSSSSSSS!

CHAPTER 4

IEEPERS CREEPERS

CREEPERS!
Don't kill it if you don't have to.
Of course I have to, Xander. These things will blow themselves up, and take us along with them.
SSSSSSSSS!
SSSSSSSSS!
SSSSSSSSS!

Hello again. I see you haven't drunk the weakening potion and eaten the golden apple yet.

No, I'm still deciding. It's not easy to give up all this witchy glamour for a chance to become a dull villager again.

Is she serious?

I don't know. It's hard to tell with witches.

If you have a home and a family you left behind, they least deserve to know you're alright.

What do you know about things like that, miner? You should MINE your own business!

a matter of fact, I know a lot about
se things. Don't you remember how
met? You and your creepers
kidnapped me!

My family was
worried sick, and
when I came back, the
librarians sent me away.
They were afraid I'd bring
danger to the village. I
stayed away as long
as I could.

Now that I'm
reunited with my
family, I appreciate
them more than ever.

That's a very
touching story, but what does
it have to do with me? My family never
understood me when I was there. I left and
lived a life of adventure I never would have
had in that stuffy village.

nderstand that,
oo. But we're
king to open our
ge so people can
e and go as they
ease. They can
on adventures
return home
out getting in
rouble.

That's where we're from.

What is your sister's name?

Do you think there's a chance this is Ole Baba's missing sister?

Bailey. Her name was Bailey.

Oh. So you're not Ole Baba's sister.

CHAPTER 5

THE
GUARDIAN BATTLE

Are you sure Merlin enchanted these helmets properly?

That guy knows what he's doing. Don't worry. We have plenty of time.

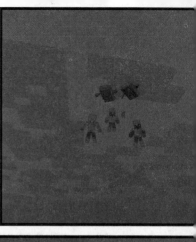

Why did it stop trying to shoot us?

The boo said all y have to d block its of sight stop it

We're lucky to have you and your book around, Xander.

Good idea. it was starting to get stuffy in there.

Is that potion of Underwater Breathing?

Xander! Where did you get that?

From Leila's pouch. I just reached in and pulled it out. Like magic.

Brilliant! Thanks, Xander!

Well, you could have thought to bring it out sooner.

I keep checking the pouch, but there hasn't been anything in it till now.

≈Sigh!≈ I never realized how much I enjoyed breathing.

Now what?

Don't get mad, but Merlin had these lined up at the door of his house when we left.

You stole boots enchanted with Depth Strider from Merlin?

Well, not exactly. He saw me take them, then turned away. We can return them when we're done!

Fine. We'll wear them becaus they're here and we hav long way to go, but don't tl I'm not going to tell Mom c Dad when we get home!

I'm not sure I'm ready for what's beyond this entrance.

I'm not sure I know what's beyond this entrance.

It's so dark...

CHAPTER 6

THE ELDER
SCROLLS

Maybe they don't exist.

Maybe we're on a fool's errand.

Or maybe we're on an adventure, and we're about to explore something we've never seen before and discover something amazing.

The hermit has a point.

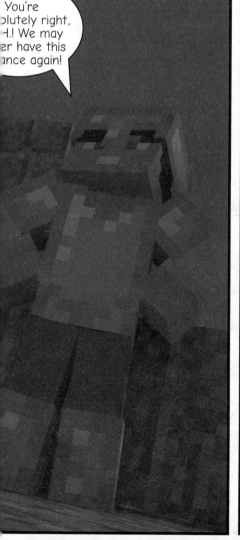

You're [abso]lutely right, [-]H.! We may [nev]er have this [ch]ance again!

We'll need to set up a base camp. Any way we can dry out a room in this place?

Actually, there is! We just need to find a sponge room. A bunch of sponges will make drying out a room quick and easy.

Let's take some of this gravel before we go--it might be useful for blocking the elder guardians.

1

Something tells me this is the sponge room.

How can you tell? It's not marked.

My amulet started glowing as soon as I leaned over it on the map.

It does make sense. This room is the only one where the entrance is in the floor and there are no other doors. That's how sponge rooms are built.

But how do we get past the elder guardians?

If we dr this, I it will hel get over Mining Fat Then we go around back and through a walls with disturbing guard

GLUG

GULP

BUUUURP

'Scuse me!

UGH GRUNT

CHOP

I'll just tand guard. ≀Yawn≀

Looks like we found it, thanks to my amulet!

Jackpot! Collect as many as you can!

Let's use this room as our base.

That's a good plan. Wet sponges are heavier than they look.

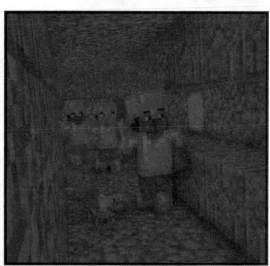

Ewww! Clownfish! I don't like them. They taste funny.

Poor Moosha. She waited so long for that drop, and it's her least favorite fish.

Less talking, m mining, y guys!

I don't feel so badly for her. Think of all the fishing she can do on our way back up to land!

What a haul!

Where's the rest of it?

The rest of what? This is the biggest treasure we've ever found!

Where the scro

CHAPTER 7

THE RETURN OF THE CREEPERS

Let's see what else I can pull out of the water!

Forget napping. Fishing is my favorite activity now. Second to eating fish, of course.

Good thing our boats stayed where we left them!

That's m... bett...

That looks like a map. But where does it lead?

I see the portal that leads to the dragon's temple. What's the X marking over here?

Oh no!

Oh no what? What does it mark? Where does it lead? Treasure?

Well, sort of. But the treas... looks like it's just...more scr... And we have to defeat th... dragon to get them.

Those must be very important scrolls if they are guarded by a dragon.

Well, at least we have a map to find th... dragon now.

Where will we get the cats from?

Oh, that's just a tiny detail.

What if we tunnel underground and attack them from below?

What if we lure them toward us?

It says here that a creeper can be blown up using flint and steel.

Great! So all we have to do lure them all away from the village in a group and set one of them off!

You mean I finally get to blow something up?

So I don't get to scare the leaves off a bunch of creepers?

Hey, cut it out! That tickles!

Hold still. Mom and Dad would kill me if I let you get blown up.

Stop squirming, dude. Your armor is going to fall off if we don't put it on you right.

Here, creeper. Come and get your little fiery snack!

SSSSSSSS

CLICK!

Look out!

You saved us! We are so grateful!

We're glad you are safe.

So how did this happen?

A few nights ago, we heard a lot of rustling outside. We were afraid to go out.

When we woke up in the morning, the creepers were guarding our houses. We couldn't leave.

Do you have any idea who could have done this?

We are simple traders. We have no enemies that we know of. But the day before we were trapped, we did have a strange visitor.

No! It couldn't be!

How strange.

strange man came to trade.
bought all our redstone from
Plum, and he kept telling us
stay home and that he was
oing to beat us to some big
ish. Or a party or something.

Good villagers stay
home. I get there first.
No one can stop me!

it a second. He had
dolls in a minecart
looked just like
u two!

Not the
Defender!

CHAPTER 8

HAPPY PUPPIES

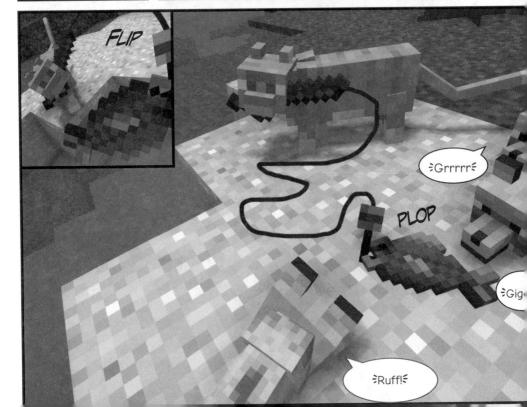

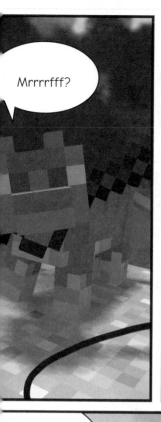

We were in the neighborhood, so we figured we'd stop by.

Are you having another adventure?

Yes! We're going to slay a dragon!

Why would you put yourself in that kind of danger?

The necklace told me to. It's getting kind of bossy.

Thank you for saving little Ayah! She always getting into trouble.

I met Phoenix the same way. She rescued me. I guess finding danger kind of runs in the family.

Have you seen the Defender yet?

We saw some strange things that seemed like his handiwork, but he can't be back. He was exiled to the Far Lands. It should have taken him years to get back here.

Not only is he back, he can also make himself INVISIBLE!

Now that's just creepy.

That's definitely someth[ing] the Defender would d[o]

We want to go on a 'venture, too, Daddy!

When you're older, young pup. When you're old enough that you don't have to be rescued every time you leave the den.

We would be honored if you spent the night here to rest up. It's the least we can do for you.

Thank you, Crystal. We would love to.

Yawn. I'd like that very much!

Wakey wakey! Eggs and...

Bakey? Yay! I'v missed staying your hut, T.H.!

It's so nice to wake up someplace safe, surrounded by friends for a change.

Yes. Thank you, Wolfie and Crystal!

You know, I have an anvil. Maybe we need to rethink our weaponry.

We have the enchanted book. We can repair our flint and steel and our armor.

I think I need to sharpen my axe and we definitely need to put Unbreaking on our shields.

Moosha, look out!

⸰CRUNCH!⸰ Got it!

What did I ever do without you, Wolfie?

⸰Shud Ugl Spide

I wish I could stay longer.

You have your prophecy to fulfill.

MOOSHA! Where are you?

Did ...meone ...l my ...me?

She can't play with you right now. She's busy playing with us. You wait your turn, Xander.

I'm sorry, pups, but we have to steal Moosha away from you right now.

CHAPTER 9

SUMMONING THE DRAGON

It's not that hard to read. We have to go through this dungeon.

I do not like the sound of that!

That's a much better weapon choice, Xander.

More spiders? I do NOT like this cave. If Wolfie were here, he'd eat those spiders for me.

I'm glad you approve, Sis. But Moosha, I'm not eating any spiders for you. Spiders are absolutely my least favorite...

SLASH

That works, too.

The only good spider is a dead spid Still think I need mo training?

Yes, we do!

This way!

Are you sure?

I don't remember a library on the path to the stronghold or the portal.

Let's make a deal. You stick to being a mindless killing machine and I'll take care of the maps.

Xander, that's not very nice!

Don't get mad, but I may or may not have accidentally read the map upside down.

He started it.

Did not!

Did too.

Enough, you two. Hey, do we have anything that needs enchanting while we're here?

Did not!

How about my fishing rod? I want Looting. And Luck. And while we're at it...

It's an enchantment table, not a genie that grants wishes, Moosha. Every time we enchant something, it costs something.

Well, you slashed a lot of zombies back there. You should at least repair that sword while we're here. Phoenix is going to be fighting a dragon, after all.

I do have the necklace.

They said it would protect you. And it hasn't steered us wrong yet.

And I have something my parents didn't have.

What? Enchanted armor?

No, I have you guys!

Let's see if we can go find that portal room.

Hey, I know where we are now. This way!

The portal room is straight ahead.

Finally, you both agree on something!

CHAPTER 10

JOURNEY TO THE END CITY

It looks so harmless, but it contains all the power of a new Ender Dragon. We need to take it with us and keep it safe.

You're right. I bet it's what the Defender is after, and he'll stop at nothing to get it.

I'm surprised he hasn't shown up yet. Glad, but surprised.

The Defender has all sorts of new powers. He could have been invisible right next to us and we wouldn't have known.

Did you sense him here?

I'm a cat, ot a dog. I can't e things that are nvisible. Sheesh!

Hey, Xander! Do the scrolls say anything about what to do next?

Let me see...The End gateway is a portal to an End city. It will lead us to the dragon's temple, where you will place the dragon egg and receive the ultimate treasure.

So that's it. We have to go in there? We have no choice?

Sadly, yes. And no.

I'm confused. Do we or don't we?

The kid said yes we do have to go in and no we don't have a choice. Weren't you listening?

POP!

Follow follow follow. Yes yes yes.

So, Xander, what other strange purple surprises await us when we get to the dragon's temple?
You're not going to like this. There appears to be a pirate ship docked just offshore.
We'll just have to hope that if there are any pirates aboard, they'll be kindly pirates who just want to bake pastries for a living.
I'm afraid the odds aren't good that's going to happen again.

I just can't believe there's a whole world as purple as my necklace.

The map doesn't say to go up there, you know.

Where's your sense of adventure, Xander? This is fun!

What do you see up there?

Oh! It's you!

Welcome, my friends! I have waited so long to see you again!

Let me guess... that's the Defender?

Phoenix, get back!

Nonsense. Come in, come in. Stay a while. I have so much to show you. So much to tell! I wanted to thank you...

When you sen me to the Far Lands...oh,, I lear so much! I hav powers, so mar powers.

ZAP!

Stay close. Let him keep talking till we figure out a plan.

I have an idea. Keep him distracted.

could see. Sometimes I had [v]isions. So clear. The necklace is [ke]y. And the dragon. And this [temp]le. It needs to be mine. [It] called out to me.

What...what did it say?

And who might you be, little village boy? Don't you know that running with this crowd can get you... eliminated?

I'll take my chances, thanks.

You're such a polite boy.

[W]hat do you [do]t with my [fr]iends?

Oh, I don't want them. I don't want them at all. But I NEED them. Curse them. I waited for someone to defeat the dragon and of course it was the girl with the glowing Ender eye.

And I came here to claim the dragon's temple, but I cannot do it alone. I need the girl and the Pollinator.

Oh, yes. I saw it all. How you created my world. You created me, boy. You parents did, anyway. And you destroyed my world...so now I want this one. It's my right.

ZAP!
Is he gone?
Something tells me we haven't se
the last of that gu

CHAPTER II

THE DRAGON TEMPLE

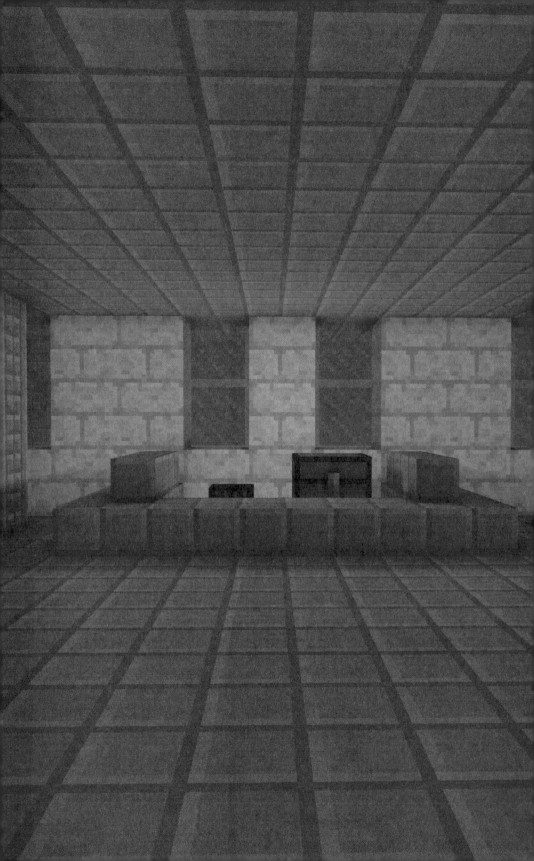

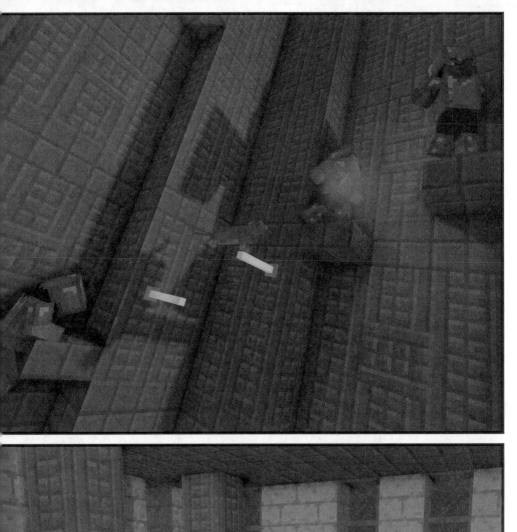

Dragon Scrolls

My necklace!

You said that already.

The prophecy has been fulfilled.

That means I'm free. No prophecy. No necklace,.

Okay scrolls, so who am I?

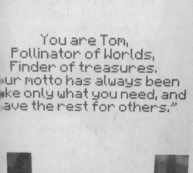

You are Tom, Pollinator of Worlds, Finder of treasures. ur motto has always been ke only what you need, and ave the rest for others."

This book doesn't know everything. That's exactly what I told the Defender when he was overmining the diamonds in the cave.

So what does it mean that I am the guardian of the dragon's temple? I don't need to stay here forever, do I?

Ask the scrolls, silly.

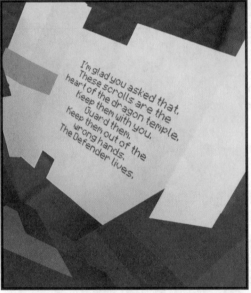

I'm glad you asked that. These scrolls are the heart of the dragon temple, keep them with you. Guard them. Keep them out of the wrong hands, The Defender lives,

What'd it say?

Good news and bad news.

The good news is, I get leave. The bad news is, I le my necklace behind. The g news is, the necklace is going to boss me arour anymore.

The bad new: is, these scro probably will st telling me what do...

Ugh! It smells like dead dragon.
I'll be happy to get back to the Overworld, where at least we know what we're up against.
Home sweet home. I've never been so happy to see ordinary spiders before.
I never thought I'd hear you say that.
SLASH!
You can come down now, Moosha.
You know how I feel abo spiders.

Oh great. Nighttime. I wonder how long we were gone for.

Where can we sleep? I don't want to spend the night in the stronghold.

Ask the scrolls!

Okay, dragon scrolls. Where can we sleep?

What's sustenance?

A mushroom will provide shelter at night and sustenance in the morning.

Food.

Good night, everyone. Good night, scrolls.

Not only does a mushroom make a great tent, it also makes a great meal!

It's filling, but I'm looking forward to a good, home-cooked meal.

I wonder what we're coming home to.

They must have made a decision by now. Are you worried?

Somehow I feel like everything is going to come out alright this time.

CHAPTER 12

UN-WELCOME HOME

Welcome back, weary travelers! Welcome, Damon and Dixie!

⸘cluuuck⸘

What about the cat? No one ever welcomes the cat.

So I guess it didn't go well with the elders?

Unfortunately, no. We have come to ask you...

We cleared the land right next to our hut in case things didn't go your way. We'd love to have you as our neighbors, if you'd like to stay.

Awesome!

Thank you, from the bottom of our hearts.

It's our pleasure. We've been out here alone for too long. It's good for Tom...I mean T.H., and it's good for us, too.

The village looks so small from here.
We had gotten so wrapped up in our lives in the village that we forgot the world could be so big and exciting.
I'm glad to be out of there. I'll miss the library and my studies, though. Can we start a school here?
Only if we could teach more than just book learning. Life skills too, okay?
It's a deal.
I agree.
There you guys are! I hear the fighting. Looks li I missed all the fun Everyone okay?